LETTERS AND MANUSCRIPTS FROM SOUTHERN AFRICA

A Survey of the Holdings of the Humanities Research Center,
The University of Texas at Austin

Richard Priebe

African and Afro-American Research Institute
The University of Texas at Austin
Austin, Texas
1972

PREFACE

Over the past twenty years the Humanities Research Center at The University of Texas at Austin has acquired a substantial manuscript collection of South African writing. Some of the holdings amount to only a few letters, but at least five contain important collections, and much of this material has yet to be used. In addition to these holdings the Center has manuscripts of Graham Greene, Joyce Cary, Havelock Ellis and other British authors whose work may also be of interest to Africanists, though only the South African authors and one Rhodesian author have been included in this bibliography.

Letters of inquiry or applications for use of the materials by qualified scholars should be addressed to The Librarian, Humanities Research Center Library, University of Texas, Austin, Texas 78712. A committee composed of faculty members from the College of Humanities will consider all requests, but it should be noted that scholars may already be working on some of the material. For example, Richard Rive is using the Schreiner collection for a doctoral dissertation at Oxford University, and Vivienne Dickson is using the Bosman collection for a doctoral dissertation at The University of Texas at Austin (see Vivienne Dickson, "Herman Charles Bosman," *The Library Chronicle of the University of Texas at Austin,* No. 4 [February, 1972], pp. 31-37).

The symbols below are the same as those used in the manuscript card catalog.

A	Autograph	C	Card
T	Typed	PC	Post Card
S	Signed	cc	Carbon Copy
I	Initialed	p	Page
Ms	Manuscript	pp	Pages
Mss	Manuscripts	ℓ	Leaf
L	Letter	ℓℓ	Leaves
FL	Form Letter	nd	No Date
N	Note	inc d	Incomplete Date
D	Document		

The symbols immediately above are used in combinations: ALS means autograph letter signed; Tccms means typed carbon copy manuscript, etc. Brackets are used to indicate that the information between them is supplied from some source other than the manuscript itself.

Inconsistencies in spelling reflect those in the manuscripts themselves or in the transcriptions on index cards of the Humanities Research Center

Richard Priebe

CONTENTS

Works

[Unidentified fragments]. Ams [2pp], nd.
[Unidentified play]. Tms, nd.
Adaptation. Ams, nd. In notebook.
The affair at Yster-Spruit. T/cc ms, nd.
Africa; Poems from Mara. Tms, nd.
Afternoon ravishment. Tms, nd.
"All through a leafy night a maden kept . . ." Ams, nd.
"All through a leafy night a maden kept . . ." [Poems]. T/cc ms, nd.
And he said unto Thomas: "Behold these hands."; The blue princess. Tms, nd.
And she called you prince; The blue princess. Tms, nd.
"And will my passing be Cused bright . . ." Ams/inc, nd.
"And will my passing be Cused bright . . ." [Poems]. T/cc ms, nd.
Anti-Semitism: A psychological illusion. Ams, nd. In notebook.
Anxious to hear. Galley proofs with numerous A corrections, nd.
"Any story (Oom Schalk Lourens said) about that half-red flower, the . . ." T/cc ms with few A revisions, nd.
Arrival. Tms with A revisions, nd.
Arrival [poems]. T/cc ms, nd.
"Art thou desolate? . . ." Ams, nd.
"Art thou desolate? . . ." [Poems]. T/cc ms, nd.
"As ek wegkee(?) . . .' Ams [in Afrikaans], nd.
Ballad; Poems from Mara. Tms, nd.
A barren tree; The blue princess. Tms, nd.
Beans growing. Tms with A revision, nd.
Beans growing [Poems]. T/cc ms, nd.
"Before the kafirs had guessed the significance of the . . ." Tms, nd.
Birds. T/cc ms, nd.
Birds [Poems]. T/cc ms, nd.
Blindness; The blue princess. Tms, nd.
Blood and sub- soiled. 2 T/cc ms, nd.
A blue cylinder. Tms, nd.
A blue cylinder. T/cc ms, nd.
A blue garden; The blue princess. Tms, nd.
The blue princess. Tms, nd. Contents: The street-walker.–And he said unto Thomas: "Behold these hands."–A girl to her lover.–A tree.–In the beginning. –Doubt.–June 9.–Lies.–An urn.–Parting.–Only.–Blindness.–First knowledge.–A blue garden.–A princess sleeping.–A barren tree.–And she called you prince.–A poet's dream.–The Orange Free State.–Ghosts.–The rival.–Memory.–Esoteric.–To Russia.–In the night.–The poet gets the boot.–Warning. –Next please.-Finis.
Blue sailings. Ams, nd. In notebook.
"The blue wind . . ." Tms, nd.
"The blue wind . . ."[Poems]. T/cc ms, nd.
Blunted weapons. Tms, nd.
Blunted weapons. T/cc ms, nd.
A Boer Rip Van Winkel. Tms with few A revisions, nd.
A Boer Rip Van Winkel. T/cc ms with few A revisions, nd.

The bridge. Tms with few A revisions, nd.
The brothers. Tms with few A revisions, nd.
The brothers. T/cc ms with A additions and revisions, nd.
Bush telegraph. Tms with few A revisions, nd.
"But it is quite different with doctors, of course. I mean, for one thing, it has . . ."
T/cc ms/inc, nd. [Page 1 missing].
Camp fires at Nagmaal. T/cc ms, nd. Typescript not by Herman Charles Bosman.
A cask of Jerepigo. Tms with A revisions, nd.
A cask of Jerepigo. Central News Agency, Ltd. TLS to L[ionel] Abrahams, 1954 December 1. Enclosed is: Copy of reader's opinion *re* A cask of Jerepigo by Herman Charles Bosman, 1954 December 1.
A cask of Jerepigo. Central News Agency, Ltd. TLS to L[ionel] Abrahams, 1955 February 1. Enclosed is: Copy of reader's opinion *re* A cask of Jerepigo by Herman Charles Bosman, nd.
"A Chinese poem". Tms, nd.
A Chinese poem; Poems from Mara. Tms, nd.
[Chivalry]. Ams, nd.
(Chivalry)[Poems]. T/cc ms, nd.
Christ's conditions. Tms with one A revision, nd.
Christ's conditions[Poems]. T/cc ms, nd.
[The clay pit]. Ams with A revisions, nd.
The clay-pit. Tms with few A revisions, nd.
The clay-pit. T/cc ms with few A revisions, nd.
A cold night. Tms, nd.
Comings. Tms, nd.
Comings. T/cc ms, nd.
Denticulated space bloom. Tms with one A revision, nd.
Denticulated space bloom. T/cc ms, nd.
"the depth of the pool. They never reached bottom, the road inspector . . ."
T/cc ms/inc, nd. Page 1 missing.
A double night. Tms, nd.
A double night. T/cc ms, nd.
Doubt; The blue princess. Tms, nd.
[Down Jules St. way]. Ams, nd. In notebook.
Dreamer. Ams, nd. Written on this: [Herman Charles Bosman], Night. Ams with few A revisions, nd.
Dreamer [Poems]. T/cc ms, nd.
"Edgar Allen Poe, poet and plagiarist, charlatan and genius—whose genius . . ."
Tms with few A revisions, nd.
Edmund Spenser. Ams, nd.
Ellaleen; Poems from Mara. Tms, nd.
Esoteric; The blue princess. Tms, nd.
"Exiled". Tms, nd.
Expedition against Majaja. Tms with few A revisions, nd.
"Fell the dew upon my lyre? . . ." Tms, nd.
"Fell the dew upon my lyre? . . ." [Poems]. T/cc ms, nd.
The Ferreira millions. T/cc ms with one A revision, nd.
Files at work. Ams, nd. In notebook.
Finis; The blue princess. Tms, nd.
First. Tms with few A revisions and two variants of stanza two, nd.

First [Poems]. T/cc ms, nd.
First knowledge; The blue princess. Tms, nd.
First served. Tms with few A revisions (3pp), Tccms (3pp), nd.
"Flesh is grass". Tms, nd.
"For I would rather have come . . ." [Poems]. T/cc ms, nd.
"For I would rather have gone . . ." Ams[1p], nd.
Friend of mine. Tms, nd.
Friend of mine [Poems]. T/cc ms, nd.
The ghost by the drift. T/cc ms with few A revisions, nd.
Ghosts; The blue princess. Tms, nd.
A girl's invocation. Tms with few A revisions, nd.
A girl's invocation [Poems]. T/cc ms, nd.
A girl to her lover; The blue princess. Tms, nd.
Gothic speech. Tms, nd.
Gothic speech [Poems]. T/cc ms, nd.
Her soul; Poems from Mara. Tms, nd.
"Here in this room, how often have you mocked me . . ." Tms, nd.
"Here in this room, how often have you mocked me . . ." [Poems]. T/cc ms, nd.
Horisonvelde. Tms [in Afrikaans], nd.
Hyperion. Ams and Tms with A revisions, nd. Pages for a proposed poem.
Hyperion. Tms, nd.
Hyperion [Poems]. T/cc ms, nd.
"I am glad to be able to put on record the fact that . . ." TmsS, 1947 November 27.
"I am older than you are . . ." Ams, nd.
"I am older than you are . . ." [Poems]. T/cc ms.
"I did not know . . ." Tms with A revisions and additions [1p], nd.
"I did not know . . ." T/cc ms, nd.
I love thee . . ." Ams, nd.
"I never go down to Fordsburg by tram without becoming excessively . . ." Tms, nd.
"I questioned but in certitude . . ." [Poems]. T/cc ms, nd.
"I took the hand of a ghost I met in Eloff Street . . ." Tms, nd.
"I took the hand of a ghost I met in Eloff Street . . ." [Poems]. T/cc ms, nd.
"I turn over all these pages . . ." Ams, nd.
"If I were broken . . ." T/cc ms, nd.
"If I were broken . . ." [Poems]. T/cc ms, nd.
In great hatred. Tms, nd.
In the beginning; The blue princess. Tms, nd.
In the night; The blue princess. Tms, nd.
Inspector Vermaak's last cast. Tms with numerous A revisions, nd.
Interrupted ritual. T/cc ms, nd.
Interrupted ritual [Poems]. T/cc ms, nd.
Intoxic. Ams, nd.
Intoxic [Poems]. T/cc ms, nd.
"It always attracted a considerable amount of attention . . ." Tms, nd.
"It is a true saying that man may scheme, but that God has the . . ." Ams with A revisions, nd.
"It is a true saying that man may plan, but that God has the last word . . ." T/cc ms with A revisions, nd.
"'It's a boundless universe,' Frikkie Terblans, the school teacher . . ." Tms/inc with A revisions, nd.

[Johannesburg Christmas Eve] : Chapter I. Tms/inc with A revisions, nd.
[Joh'burg]. Ams, nd. In notebook.
John Dryden (1631-1700). Ams, nd.
June 9; The blue princess. Tms, nd.
The Kafir drum: [Version A]. Tms with few A revisions, nd. Typescript not by Herman Charles Bosman. Translated from Afrikaans.
The Kaffir drum: [Version B]. Tms with few A corrections, nd. Typescript not by Bosman. Edited version based on Bosman's Kafir drum: [Version A] and a fragment in English.
"Knowledge is power and a grey cat asleep . . ." T/cc ms, nd. Earlier version of: Herman Charles Bosman, "Luck in the square stone . . ." Included in [Herman Charles Bosman] [Poems]. T/cc ms, nd.
"Knowledge is power and a grey cat asleep . . ." [Poems]. T/cc ms, nd.
Laugh that one off [Poems]. T/cc ms, nd.
Leaning destiny. Tms with two A revisions, nd. Written on this: [Herman Charles Bosman] Sappho's speech. Tms with one A revision, nd.
Leaning destiny [Poems]. T/cc ms, nd.
"Let the world around me be flat . . ."[Poems]. T/cc ms, nd.
"Let the veld around me be . . ." Ams, nd.
Poem: "Let us find candles for the nativity . . ." [Poems]. T/cc ms, nd.
Lies; The blue princess. Tms, nd.
Life and death. T/cc ms, nd.
Lost pavements. Ams, nd. In notebook.
Louis Wassenaar. Tms/inc with A revisions, nd. Pages 1-38.
"The luck in the square stone . . ." Ams, nd.
"The luck in the square stone . . ." Tms, nd.
"Luck in the square stone . . ."; "Knowledge is power and a grey cat asleep . . ." T/cc ms, nd. Earlier version of: Herman Charles Bosman, "Luck in the square stone . . ." Included in: [Herman Charles Bosman] [Poems]. T/cc ms, nd.
"The luck in the square stone . . ." [Poems]. T/cc ms, nd.
Magic; Poems from Mara. Tms, nd.
Poems from Mara. Tms, nd. Contents: Ellaleen.–Magic.–A Chinese poem.–The virgin birth.–Her soul.–Ballad.–Oorlog.–Yecheved.–Africa.
"Marthinus Taljaard lived in a house that his grandfather had built . . ." Ams with A revisions, nd. In notebook.
Memory. Tms, nd.
Memory; The blue princess. Tms, nd.
Memory [Poems]. T/cc ms, nd.
Mental trouble. Tms with A revisions, nd.
The missionary. Tms with A revisions, nd.
[The missionary: additions]. Ams of additions A-C, nd.
The missionary: additions. Tms with few A revisions, nd.
The murderer. Tms with A revisions, nd.
[The murderess]. Ams, nd.
My first love. Tms with A revisions, nd. Typescript not by Herman Charles Bosman. Translated from Afrikaans.
"My own case is like this: I got wet in the rain and a couple of days . . ." Tms with A revisions and additions, nd.
[Nameless here]. Ams, nd.
(Nameless here) [Poems]. T/cc ms, nd.
New elder. Tms, nd.

Next please; The blue princess. Tms, nd.
Night. Ams, nd. Written on: [Herman Charles Bosman] Dreamer. Ams, nd.
Night [Poems]. T/cc ms, nd.
1943. Ams, nd. In notebook.
"'No, it's not right,' Gysbert van Tonder agreed with At Naude. 'I can . . ."
 Tms with A revisions, nd.
"Not yet may I arise . . ." Ams, nd.
"Not yet may I arise . . ." [Poems]. T/cc ms, nd.
[Notes]. 6 groups of A and T notes for unidentified mss, nd.
Notes for stories and odd pages. 11 A, T and T/cc notes and inc mss, nd.
"Old am I in years and wisdom and . . ." Tms with A revisions, nd.
"Old am I in years and wisdom and . . ." [Poems]. T/cc ms, nd.
Old Transvaal story. T/cc ms with A revisions, nd.
[On looking through some ancient papers]. Ams, nd. In notebook.
Only; The blue princess. Tms, nd.
Oorlog; Poems from Mara. Tms, nd.
The Orange Free State; The blue princess. Tms, nd.
Orders for novel, "Jacaranda in the night," by H. C. Bosman, nd.
"The other day I got ill . . ." Tms with few A revisions, nd.
Other raiment. Ams, nd. In notebook.
Parting; The blue princess. Tms, nd.
Past roses and brown water. Tccms (6pp), nd. Original title deleted: When the
 heart is eager.
Pavement patter. T and T/cc ms with A revisions, nd.
Ploughed field. Tms, nd.
Ploughed field [Poems]. T/cc ms, nd.
Poem: "I don't say the Fates were actuated . . ." Tms with one A revision, nd.
Poem: "It's only when I have forgotten the small . . ." Tms, nd.
Poem: "It's only when I have forgotten the small . . ." [Poems]. T/cc ms, nd.
[Poem]: "Let us find candles for the nativity . . ." Tms [1p], Tccms [1p], nd.
[Poem]: "Let us find candles for the nativity. . ." T/cc ms, nd.
Poem: "No, I don't want to tell any more stories . . ." Tms with few A revisions, nd.
Poem: "No, I don't want to tell any more stories . . ." [Poems]. T/cc ms, nd.
[Poems]. T/cc ms, nd. Contents: Birds.–Gothic speech.–"The wind across the veld is thin . . ."–Sermon in great malice.–Friend of mine.–"The blue wind . . ." –Laugh that one off.–"When the moon walks . . ."–Beans growing.–Memory. –"Here in this room, how often have you mocked me . . ."–Recovery from mental illness.–Wheels within wheels.–Poems: "No, I don't want to tell any more stories . . ."–Arrival.–The poet.–Christ's conditions.–Interrupted ritual.–"I took the hand of a ghost I met in Eloff Street . . ."–A girl's invocation.–First.–"Old am I in years and wisdom and . . ."–Sappho's speech.–"If I were broken . . ."–"The sky is a grey tent . . ."–"The luck in the square stone . . ."–"Knowledge is power and a grey cat asleep . . ."–"A white uninflected flower . . ."–Poem: "It's only when I have forgotten the small . . ."–Leaning destiny.–Youth.–Royalty of grass.–"Who will look after me . . ."–"Fell the dew upon my lyre? . . ."–(World noise).–(Chivalry).–(nameless here).–"Let the world around me be flat . . ."–"Art thou desolate? . . ."–"They came together the gay . . ."–Night.–Intoxic.–Dreamer.–"Veld inhabited by silence."–"I am older than you are . . ."–"For I would rather have come . . ."–"And will my passing be Cused bright . . ."–"I questioned but

in certitude . . ."–"Not yet may I arise . . ."–"Should I live longer yet this would I see . . ."–"All through a leafy night a maden kept . . ."–Song of the nations.–Ploughed field.–Hyperion.–Poem: "Let us find candles for the nativity . . ."–Scientific observation.–Sermon in great malice.
The poet. T/cc ms with A revisions, nd.
The poet [Poems]. T/cc ms, nd.
The poet gets the boot; The blue princess. Tms, nd.
A poet's dream; The blue princess. Tms, nd.
A princess sleeping; The blue princess. Tms, nd.
"The radio mystery serial to which he had been listening-in . . ." Ams, nd.
The recognising blues. TmsS with few A revisions, nd.
Recovery from mental illness [Poems]. T/cc ms, nd.
The red coat. Tms with few A revisions, nd.
The red coat. T/cc ms, nd.
Red cock-crow. Tms, nd.
Red cock[-crow]. T/cc ms, nd.
The rival; The blue princess. Tms, nd.
Rivier-Af Verkoop. T/cc ms [In Afrikaans], nd.
Romance. Tms, nd.
Romaunt of the Smuggler's daughter. T/cc ms, nd.
Royalty of grass [Poems]. T/cc ms, nd.
[Rubiajat van Omar Khajjam]. Galley proofs, nd. Translation into Afrikaans.
Tr. Rubiajat van Omar Khajjam. 2 Tms/inc with A emendations and notes, nd. Translation into Afrikaans.
[Rubiajat van Omar Khajjam]. Tccms/inc [6pp], nd. Translation into Afrikaans. Included with this: Tms/fragment [1p] and Tccms/fragment [1p].
Sappho's speech. Tms with one A revision, nd. Written on: [Herman Charles Bosman] Leaning destiny. Tms with two A revisions, nd.
Sappho's speech. [Poems]. T/cc ms, nd.
Scientific observation. Tms, nd.
Scientific observation [Poems]. T/cc ms, nd.
"Seed". Tms, nd.
[The selons-rose]. Ams with A revisions, nd. In notebook.
The selons-rose. Tms with few A revisions, nd.
Sermon in great malice. Tms, nd.
Sermon in great malice [Poems]. T/cc ms, nd.
"Should I live longer yet then would I see . . ." Ams with A revisions, nd.
"Should I live longer yet this would I see . . ." [Poems]. T/cc ms, nd.
Shy young man. Tms with few A revisions, nd.
"Sitting back comfortably in his host's armchair, the big-game hunter was . . ." Ams and Tms/inc, nd. Notes for unfinished story.
"The sky is a grey tent . . ." Tms, nd.
"The sky is a grey tent . . ." [Poems]. T/cc ms, nd.
"So for a whole week, slowly and with great difficulty, they journeyed . . ." Tms with A revisions, nd.
"So for a whole week, slowly and with great difficulty, they journeyed . . ." T/ccms, nd.
Sold down the river. Ams with A revisions, nd. In notebook.
Sold down the river. TmsS with A revisions, nd.
Sold down the river. T/ccms, nd.

Solemn wind. Tms, nd.
Solemn wind. T/ccms, nd.
Song of the nations. Ams, nd.
Song of the nations [Poems]. T/cc ms, nd.
"The sooth-sayer". Tms with one A line, nd.
South. Tms with few A revisions, nd.
South. T/ccms with A revisions, nd. Early version.
"Stefanus Malherbe had difficulty in getting access to the . . ." Tms with numerous A revisions, nd.
"[Stefanus Malherbe had difficulty in getting access to the . . .]" T/ccms with numerous A revisions, nd.
[The stile]. Ams with A revisions, nd. In notebook.
The stile. T/ccms with few A revisions, nd.
The story of Hester Van Wyk. Tms, nd. Typescript not by Herman Charles Bosman.
Street-woman. Tms with few A revisions, nd.
Street-woman. T/ccms, nd.
The street-walker; The blue princess. Tms, nd.
Susanna & the play-actors. Tms with A revisions and additions, nd.
A Tale writ in water. Tms (5pp), nd.
"That film that was showing . . ." Tms with A revisions (17pp), nd. Written on verso of pp 15-17: Composition in Afrikaans.
"There was one convict . . ." Tms with A emendations (8pp), nd.
"There was something oddly familiar . . ." A and Tms with A emendations (4pp), nd.
"They came together the gay . . ." Ams/inc/mutilated [1p], nd.
"They came together the gay . . ." [Poems]. T/cc ms, nd.
"They raised much dust from the earth floor of the . . ." Ams, nd.
To Russia; The blue princess. Tms, nd.
The Traitor's wife. Tccms with Ams/final line (6pp), nd.
A Tramp, dead in John Ware Park. Tms [1p], nd.
A tree; The blue princess. Tms, nd.
Tryst by the Vaal. Tms (5pp), Tccms (5pp), nd.
Underworld. Ams with A revisions (13pp), Tccms (9pp), nd.
An urn; The blue princess. Tms, nd.
"A Vein of humor . . ." Accms/inc [1p], Tccms (2pp), nd. Autobiographical sketch.
"Veld inhabited by silence" [Poems]. T/cc ms, nd.
Vernietiging (?). Ams [In Afrikaans], nd. In notebook.
The virgin birth; Poems from Mara. Tms, nd.
Visitors to Platrand. Tccms with A emendations (7pp), nd.
Vista of bees. Tms (2pp), Tccms (2pp), nd.
Warning; The blue princess. Tms, nd.
"The Way Ben Myburg suddenly . . ." Tms with A revisions (9pp), nd.
"We did not like the sound . . ." A and Tms with A revisions [14pp], nd.
"What I believe about a story (Oom Schalk Lourens said) is that it should really . . ." Ams, nd. In notebook.
Wheels within wheels. Tms with A emendations [1p], nd.
Wheels within wheels [Poems]. T/cc ms, nd.
"When I came out . . ." Ams with A revisions (7pp), nd.
"When I was asked to say . . ." 2 Tms/drafts/inc with A emendations [7pp], nd.
"When the moon walks . . ." Tms with A corrections [1p], nd.

"When the moon walks . . ." [Poems]. T/cc ms, nd.
" A White uninflected flower . . ." Tms [1p], nd.
"A white uninflected flower . . ." [Poems]. T/cc ms, nd.
"Who will look after me . . ." Tms [1p], Tccms[1p], nd.
"Who will look after me . . ." [Poems]. T/cc ms, nd.
[Willemsdorp]: Version A. Tms/inc with few A revisions, nd.
[Willemsdorp]: Version A. T/ccms/inc, nd.
[Willemsdorp]: Version B. Tms/inc, nd.
[Willemsdorp]: Version B. T/ccms/inc, nd.
"The Wind across the veld . . ." Tms with A emendations [1p], nd.
"The wind across the veld is thin . . ." [Poems]. T/cc ms, nd.
The Wind in the trees. Tccms (6pp), nd.
Wingspread & bedspread. Tms [1p], nd.
Without a bit. Tms (2pp), Tccms (2pp), nd.
World noise. Ams with A emendations [1p], nd.
(World noise) [Poems]. T/cc ms, nd.
Yecheved; Poems from Mara. Tms, nd.
"You can always get people . . ." A and Tms/drafts/inc [23pp], nd.
Youth. Tms [1p], nd.
Youth [Poems]. T/cc ms, nd.

Letters

2 TLS to Lionel Abrahams. 1947 May 24, 1947 June 18.
AL/draft to Roy Campbell, nd.
TLS to Central News Agency, Ltd. [addressed to N. C. Wynne], 1946 October 25. Attached is: List of short stories by H. C. Bosman submitted herewith.
TLS to [Central News Agency, Ltd.], 1947 January 10.
3 TLS to Central News Agency, Ltd. [addressed to W. Wolpert], 1947 January 4, 1947 January 25, 1947 October 25.
2 TLS to The Dassie Books, 1949 April 21, 1949 May 1.
TL/cc to Klopp (Erika) Verlag, 1948 April 30.
ALS to Adèle Legard, 1951 June 15.
TL/cc to Margaret L. Macpherson, 1951 August 23.
TL/copy to [Alan] Paton, nd.
A notes for letter to [Bernard] Sachs, nd. Included with this: Explanatory note by H. R. Lake.

Miscellaneous

Unidentified author. Report on short stories by G. to H. C. Bosman. Tccms, nd.
Unidentified author. AL/draft to [unidentified recipient], nd.
Unidentified author. AN *re* H[erman] C[harles] B[osman], typescripts, nd.
Unidentified author. ALS to Helena [Bosman], nd.
Unidentified author. ALS to Herman [Charles Bosman], nd.
Unidentified author. TL to Central News Agency, Ltd. [addressed to W. Wolpert], 1954 December 15.
Unidentified author. TL/cc to H[oward] B. Timmins, 1948 April 14.
Lionel [Abrahams]. TLS to [Herman Charles] Bosman, 1947 May 30.
Afrikaanse Kulturele Leserskring. TL/copy Colin Read-McDonald to Herman C[harles] Bosman, 1947 April 14.
Afrikaanse Pers Boekhandel. 6 TLS to H[erman] C[harles] Bosman, 1948-1950.

Baronne G. de Bellet. TL/copy to [unidentified recipient], 1948 February 27.
[Notebook I of miscellaneous material]. Ams, nd. Bound.
[Notebook II of miscellaneous material]. Ams, nd. Bound.
[Notes and fragments]. 14 A and T notes, nd.
[Tables of contents]. 3 Amss [3pp], 1 Tccms [1p], nd.
Pierre [Bosman]. 3 TLS to Herman [Charles Bosman], 1949 October 22, 1949 December 8, 1951 March 4.
The British Broadcasting Corporation. 4 TLS to Herman Charles Bosman, 1949 March 31-July 11.
D. Bruce. ALS to [Herman Charles] Bosman, 1950 March 26.
Guy Buther (?). ALS to Herman [Charles] Bosman, 1950 May 10.
Roy Campbell, 1901-1957. 3 ALS, TLS with 2 photostat/copies to Herman C[harles] Bosman, 2 nd, 1949.
Central News Agency, Ltd. 8 TLS to Lionel Abrahams, 1954-1957. Attached to TLS 1954 December 1 and 1955 February 1: Copies of reader's opinion of Bosman's A Cask of Jerepigo.
Central News Agency, Ltd. TL/copy to *Baronne* G. de Bellet, 1948 April 9.
Central News Agency, Ltd. TLS to H[erman] C[harles] Bosman, 1946 November 28. Pasted in scrapbook.
Central News Agency, Ltd. 5 Tcc Royalty statements to H[erman] C[harles] Bosman, 1947-1949.
Central News Agency, Ltd. TL to H[erman] C[harles] Bosman, 1948 January 26. Pasted in scrapbook.
Central News Agency, Ltd. TLS to H[erman] C[harles] Bosman, 1948 February 23. Pasted in scrapbook.
Central News Agency, Ltd. 19 TLS to H[erman] C[harles] Bosman, 1948-1951.
Central News Agency, Ltd. TccL to Gt. Brit. Overseas Press Services, 1950 February 9.
Common Sense. TLS Amelia Levy to Helena Bosman, 1951 October 29.
F. M. Crouse. TLS to H[erman Charles] Bosman, 1952 April 30.
Dassie Books. 2 TLS to Herman [Charles] Bosman, 1949 April 28, 1951 June 13.
Anthony Delius (?). TLS to [Herman Charles] Bosman, 1940 January 16.
Die Brandwag. TLS to H[erman] C[harles] Bosman, 1947 May 28.
Die Ruiter. TLS to H[erman] C[harles] Bosman, 1948 January 1. Pasted in scrapbook.
Amy Fisk. ALS to [Herman Charles] Bosman, 1949 September 21.
The Forum. TLS to H[erman] C[harles] Bosman, 1950 March 31.
Deborah J. Gatward. ALS to [Herman Charles] Bosman, nd.
Charles Glimpton. TLS to Herman [Charles Bosman], 1950 June 22.
Phyllis Gopalan. TL to Herman Charles [Bosman], 1949 November 19.
Gt. Brit. Overseas Press Services. TLS to The Editor, Spotlight, 1951 May 23.
B. J. Green. TLS to Herman [Charles] Bosman, 1949 November 17.
Harper & Brothers. TLS Cass Canfield to Herman Charles Bosman, 1949 March 18.
Harper & Brothers. 2 TLS Cass Canfield to [Margaret L.] Macpherson, 1949 May 11, 1949 June 9.
Hansie and Pat Hart. ALS to Helena and Herman [Bosman], nd.
Josine. ALS to Helena and Herman [Bosman], 1951 January 20. In Afrikaans.
Klopp (Erika) Verlag. TLS to Central News Agency, Ltd., 1948 March 15.
Klopp (Erika) Verlag. 6 TLS to Herman Charles Bosman, 1948 May 9-December 19.

Herbert Kretzmer. ALS, 2 TLS to Herman C[harles] Bosman, 1950 January 17, 1950 February 23, 1951 September 20.
Michael Krige. ALS to Herman [Charles] and Helena [Bosman], 1951 January 26.
Uys Krige. ALS to Herman [Charles Bosman], nd.
H. R. [Lake]. ALS to Herman [Charles Bosman], 1950 November 26.
H. R. Lake. 3 A notes S *re* Herman Charles Bosman, nd.
Jessica Liebson. ALS, TLS to H[erman] C[harles] Bosman, 1950 August 23, 1950 October 25.
Phyllis [Lurgell]. ALS, 2 TLS to Herman [Charles Bosman], nd, 1951 June 2, 1951 July 16.
Roy [Martin] Macnab, 1923- . ALS to [Herman Charles] Bosman, 1949 December 5.
Margaret L. Macpherson. 2 TLS to Herman Charles Bosman, 1949 September 9, 1951 October 10.
Gordon Makepeace. TLS to H[erman] C[harles] Bosman, 1948 February 27.
G. Mullyn (?). ALS to [Herman Charles] Bosman, 1948 February 9. Pasted in scrapbook.
Cecil Napier. TLS to H[erman] C[harles] Bosman, 1948 June 5.
Richard Nash. ALS to [Herman Charles] Bosman, 1949 September 28.
On Parade. TLS to H[erman] C[harles] Bosman, 1948 September 21.
Alan Paton. ALS to [Herman Charles] Bosman, 1949 March 29.
Miss S. Paver. 2 ALS to [Herman Charles] Bosman, 1950 April 5, 1950 May 20.
[Bernard Sachs], 1905- . ALS to Herman [Charles Bosman], nd.
[Bernard Sachs], 1905- . ANS to Herman [Charles Bosman], nd. Enclosed is: [Bernard Sachs], Multitude of dreams: unpublished pages. Page proofs with A notes and revisions, nd. Multitude of dreams: unpublished pages. Galley proofs with A notes and revisions, nd.
St. John Committee for the Prevention of Blindness. TLS "by Roy Macnab," to [Herman Charles] Bosman, 1949 November 1.
Vera Sawyer. Telegram/copy to [Herman Charles Bosman], 1951 December 24.
Hazel Simms. TLS to Herman [Charles Bosman], 1951 May 4.
F. D. Sinclair. ALS to [Herman Charles] Bosman, 1951 August 24.
South African Broadcasting Corporation. TLS to Herman Charles Bosman, 1948 January 10. Pasted in scrapbook.
South African Broadcasting Corporation. 3 TLS to Herman Charles Bosman, 1948 January 9, 1950, 1950 January 20.
Spotlight. 2 TLS to H[erman] C[harles] Bosman, 1951 June 6, 1951 June 14.
Spotlight. 2 receipts to Herman C[harles] Bosman, _____ February, 1949 December.
The Star. Receipt to Herman Charles Bosman, 1949 August 8.
Lena Stepath. 2 TLS to [Herman Charles] Bosman, _____ December 5, 1949 February 19.
[D. K. Tandiwe]. TLS "by secretary" to [Herman Charles] Bosman, 1949 September 14.
Victoria Tandiwe. TLS to [Herman Charles] Bosman, 1950 May 1.
The Transvaal Education Department. TLS to H[erman] C[harles] Bosman, 1942 September 25.
Union of South Africa. Expenditure receipt to H[erman Charles] Bosman, 1950 May 17.
University of the Witwatersrand. 2 ALS to [Herman Charles] Bosman, 1948

March 11, 1950 April 8.

University of the Witwatersrand. Council of Cultural Societies. TLS to [Herman Charles] Bosman, 1950 June 13.

University of Witwatersrand. Certification of Herman Charles Bosman, 1940 October 2.

"Vera." ALS to H[erman] C[harles] B[osman], 1949 July 24. Written on this is ANS by H. R. Lake.

Ada Volhand. 3 ALS, 2 TLS to Helena and Herman [Bosman], 1950-1951.

Mary [Morrison Webster]. TLS to Herman [Charles Bosman], 1947 December 16, Pasted in scrapbook.

Mary [Morrison Webster]. TLS to Helena [Bosman] and Herman [Charles Bosman], 1949 July 5.

Mary [Morrison Webster]. 2 TLS to Herman [Charles Bosman], nd, 1950 August 23.

Sampie de Wet. 2 ALS to Herman [Charles Bosman], 1947 April 14, 1948 February 23.

Mrs. G. Wheeler. ALS to Herman [Charles Bosman] and Helena [Bosman], 1949 October 21.

H. Zandstra. ALS to H[erman] C[harles] Bosman, 1946 August 5.

ROY CAMPBELL, 1901-1957

Works

[Untitled poem]: From the Spanish of Luis [Vaz] de Camões. Ams [2pp], nd.

[Unidentified poems]. Ams/fragments with A emendations [9pp], nd.

[Unidentified prose work]. 2 Ams/fragments [2pp], nd.

[Unidentified works]. 3 Ams/prose fragments [1 page each], nd.

The art of poetry by [Quintus Horatius Flaccus] Horace. Translated by Roy Campbell. AmsS with A revisions (27 pp), nd. Written in paper covered exercise book.

Autobiography in fifty kicks (To A. F. Tschiffely) [poem]. Ams with A emendations and ANS to Tom Moult [2pp on 1ℓ], 1953 (Collares).

Banderillas de fuego [article]. AmsS with A revisions and notes (4pp), nd. On translation of Garcia Lorca poems.

Choosing a mast. Ams [1p], nd. Included with this: Tms copy.

Collected poems, Vol. III: Translations. Tccms [172pp], nd. Written on cover: Edith Sitwell's copy.

Collected poems [Richard Church], 1893- [Review of 11 books of poetry]. Tccms with A emendations [4pp] [c. 1949]. Includes reviews of The canticle of the rose by Edith Sitwell, Collected poems by Roy Campbell, To awaken Pegasus by Lord Dunsany, And in the human heart by Conrad Aiken, The edge of being by Stephen Spender.

Dylan Thomas: The war years. AmsS [1p], [1954]. With this: Printed version from Shenandoah Magazine. Included with: His The poetry of Dylan Thomas. Boxed.

Excuse for want of anything better. AmsS [1p], _____ April 24. In: Visitors' Book of the Poetry Society. University of London. Goldsmiths' College. Evening Literary Department.

Familiar daemon. AmsS [1p], nd. Written on verso of Song.

The Flaming Terrapin. n.d.

[Les fleurs du mal by Charles Pierre Baudelaire. Translated by Roy Campbell]. Ams with A revisions, nd. Translations of 40 poems.

From Orpheus (Part II). Ams with few A emendations [1p], nd. Included with this: Ams/draft of 5th stanza with title Scars on the rump; written on page with AL/draft/fragment [1p]. No date.

"Here comes that Rocky Mountain fellow . . ." Ams/inc [1p], nd.

Homage to the great Ezra. Ams [1p], nd. Written on card.

[The House of Bernarda Alba by Federico García Lorca. Translated by Roy Campbell]. Ams with A emendations (87pp), nd.

"I ask, 'Why has it dawned another day?'" Ams with A emendations [1p], nd.

"In his self-portrait in the nude . . ." Ams/inc [1p], nd.

Lecture at Salamanca. Ams/fragment with A emendations (4pp), nd. In Spanish.

El Mio Cid. Ams with A emendations [1p], nd. Written on this: ANS to Violeta. No date. Included with this: 2 Ams/fragments of the poem. No date.

[El Mio Cid]. In memoriam A. F. Tschiffely. AmsS [1p], nd. Included with this: 3 Ams/drafts/inc. No date.

"Now almond groves are fleeced in flying spray . . ." Ams [1p], nd.

On being asked by a schoolboy why I wasn't included in Mr. Wayward's Cassowary Anthology. Ams [1p], nd. Included with this: Ams/variant version. [1p]. No date.

Orpheus. Ams (lp), nd. Included with this: 2 Ams/drafts with A emendations [1 page each]. No date.

The palm. AmsI with A note S at end [2pp], nd. Included with this: Tms/copy.

Poems of St. John of the cross. AmsS with A note S [41pp], nd. "only extant manuscript". Boxed.

Poems of St. John of the cross. Derek Patmore, 1908- , [Review of] St. John of the Cross; Spanish text with a translation by Roy Campbell. Tccms (4pp), nd. For The Month.

The poetry of Dylan Thomas. AmsS with A additions and A note I [5pp], [1946]. Included with this: Tccms inscribed to Caitlin and photostatic copy of this item; AmsS Dylan Thomas: The war years [1p] and printed version from Shenandoah Magazine [Spring, 1954]. Boxed.

[The poetry of Luiz de Camões]. Tccms [12pp], nd. Extract from longer work.

The pomegranates. Ams [2pp], nd. Included with this: Tms/copy.

Renunciation. Ams/inc with deletions [1p], nd.

[Review of] One is one by P. D. Cummins. AmsS with A emendations [4pp], nd.

[Review of] One is one by P. D. Cummins. Galley proof with A corrections [1p], nd.

Song. AmsS [1p], nd. Written on verso: Familiar daemon.

"The stars, like kisses, have devoured the night . . ." AmsS [1p], nd.

Toril [poem]. AmsS with A emendations [2pp], nd.

The trickster of Seville [play]. Ams/inc with A revisions [13pp], nd. Included with this: Another Ams/fragment version with title The scoundrel of Seville, [5pp]. No date.

Trompasas a los trompasos. Ams Christmas greetings verse to Peter, Christopher and Marjorie [2pp], nd.

Vision of Our Lady over Toledo. Tms (7pp), Tccms (7pp), nd.

Le voyage. Ams/workings [5pp in notebook], nd. Also written with this: Ams/workings of 2 unidentified poems.

Letters

AL/unfinished to [unidentified recipient], nd.

AL/draft/inc to unidentified recipient, nd. In Spanish.

AL/draft/inc to unidentified recipient, nd. Included with this: A note for the draft.

AL/draft/inc to unidentified recipient *re* Campbell's knowledge of the battle of the Alcazar, nd.

ALS to unidentified recipient *re* controversy by letters, nd.

AL/inc to [unidentified recipient] John, nd.

3 AL/drafts/inc to unidentified editor-recipient *re* French writers, nd.

ALS/draft to unidentified editor-recipient *re* misprint in his review of Aldington's Mistral, nd. Included with this: 2 AL/drafts/inc. No date.

AL/draft/inc to unidentified editor-recipient *re* progress, nd.

AL/draft/inc to unidentified editor-recipient *re* publication of poem, nd.

ALS/draft to unidentified editor-recipient *re* review of Camilo Cela book, nd. Included with this: 3 AL/drafts/inc. No date.

2 AL/drafts/inc with A revisions to unidentified recipient *re* review of new Spanish poets, nd.

AL/draft/inc to unidentified editor-recipient *re* reviewer Eberhart and Campbell's fascism, nd. Included with this: 3 A fragments on same topic.

4 AL/drafts/inc to unidentified editor recipient *re* reviewer of Newer poets of Spain, nd.

ALS/inc to unidentified recipient *re* rhinoceros horn, nd.

AN to unidentified recipient *re* T. E. Lawrence, nd.

AL/draft/inc to Alan, nd.

APCS to [Terence Ian Fytton Armstrong], "John Gawsworth." 1947 January 23 [postmark].

4 ALS to [Edmund Charles] Blunden, 3 nd, _____ May 30.

3 ALS, TLS, with 2 photostat/copies, to Herman C[harles] Bosman, 2-nd, 2-1949.

ALS to [Jocelyn] Brooke, nd.

ALS to Archie [Campbell], nd.

21 ALS, 1 ALI, 1 AL, 1 AL/inc, 3 APCS to Mary Campbell, 16 nd, 3 inc d, 1943-1954. Included with these: Envelopes to Tullah Hanley and envelope and sheet with A notes *re* these by Tullah Hanley.

12 ALS, 1 ALI to Mrs. Sam G. Campbell, 12 nd, 1943-1946. Included with these: Annotations by Tullah Hanley on separate sheet.

3 ALS to [Teresa] Campbell, 2 nd, 1943 November 12. Written on one undated letter: ANS by Mary Campbell; also enclosed with it pencil sketch by Roy Campbell. Enclosed with these: 2 ALS Teresa. Campbell Custódio, one to Tullah Hanley, one to her sister Amy, 1965 March 29 & April 20.

7 ALS, 1 ALS/photographic copy, 1 APCS "Dad" to Teresa Campbell, 7 nd. 1937 June 30 [postmark], 1943 September 17 [postmark], 1944 January 6, 1944 March 12.

ALS to Charles, nd.

ALS to Richard Church, nd.

ALS to Richard Church, nd.

2 ALS to Ronald [Frederick Henry] Duncan, nd.

AL/draft/inc to [Thomas Stearns] Eliot, nd.

2 ALS to [Edward] Garnett, nd.

4 ALS to Edward Garnett, _____, About Nov. 20, _____, Aug. 24, 1924 Sept. 9, 1925 Feb. 11.

Telegram to Edward Garnett, 1924 Jan. 12.
Christmas card S to [Thomas] Ed[ward] Hanley, [1955 December 14]. To Ed and Tullah from Roy and Mary Campbell. Contains an ink drawing, probably by Campbell.
AL/draft/unfinished to [Thomas Edward and Tullah Hanley], nd. A notes I by Mary Campbell at bottom.
4 ALS, 2 APCS to [Thomas] Ed[ward] and Tullah Hanley, 5 nd, 1956 July 5.
ALS to Tullah [Hanley], _____ April 7.
ALS to Jim Hawthorn, nd.
AL/draft/inc to Dr. Heller, nd.
AL/draft/inc to Brian [Higgins], nd.
AL/draft to Henry Regnery Co. *re* Rebecca West's The meaning of treason, nd. Written on T copy of letter from The Viking Press to Henry Regnery Co. *re* Campbell's criticism of the book. 1956 Aug. 23.
ALS to [John] Lehmann, nd. Written on this: ANI Lehmann to secretary.
ALS to [Thomas] Moult, nd.
8 ALS, 1 TLS, 1 APCS to Herbert [Edward] Palmer, nd. Palmer dates these c. 1927-c. 1947.
ALS to F[rederic] Prokosh [sic.], nd.
ALS to Rheinhart [?],- nd.
AL/fragment to Rob, nd.
ALS to [Nesta Sawyer], nd.
14 ALS, 1 AL to *Dame* Edith Sitwell, nd.
3 ALS, 1 APCS to *Dame* Edith Sitwell, 2 nd, 1952 October 7, 1954 May 7 [postmark].
TLS to [Stephen] Spender, 1946 June 11.
2 ALS to [Leonard Alfred George] Strong, nd.
AL/draft/inc to Tambi, nd.
ALS to Aimé [Tschiffely], 1952 Oct. 6.

Letters—Recipient
[Herman Charles Bosman]. AL draft to Roy Campbell, nd.
[Thomas] Ed[ward] Hanley. 3 TccL to Roy Campbell, 1956 August 4, 1956 October 1, 1956 October 27.
Wyndham Lewis, 1886-1957. 3 ALI, TLS to Roy Campbell, nd, 1936 Aug. 13, 1936 Oct. 25, 1951 July 14.
Bertram Rota. ALS to Roy Campbell, 1956 June 29.
[Dame] Edith [Sitwell], 1887-1964. ALS to Roy [Campbell], 1956 September 5. A annotations by Campbell.
Stephen Spender, 1909- . TccLS to [Roy] Campbell, _____ June 2.
The Bodley Head. 2 TLS Max Reinhardt to *Dame* Edith Sitwell *re* introduction to Roy Campbell translations, 1959 April 13, 1959 April 30.

Miscellaneous
[Unidentified author], [Review of] Poems of St. John of the Cross: Spanish text with a translation by Roy Campbell. Tms/inc [1p], nd.
Mary Campbell. 2 ALS to [Jacob] Schwartz, _____ January 20, _____ February 23.
[Unidentified recipient]. Ams/fragment with A revisions [1p], nd. Autobiographical incident.

[Unidentified recipient]. Ams/fragment with A emendations [1p], nd. Critical comments on poetry.
Manuscript notebooks. Amss with A revisions [31 exercise books], nd.
[Notebooks I]. Ams exercise books with A revisions [4 notebooks], nd. Contains drafts of poems, letters and prose works.
[Poetic workings I]. Ams/fragments with A revisions, nd. Pages cut from notebooks with fragmentary drafts of poetic works.
[Poetic workings II]. Ams/fragments and drafts with A revisions, nd. Numbered pages cut from notebook, many missing. Contains drafts of "A modern Orpheus" and "Il mio cid."
[Poetic workings III]. Ams/fragments and drafts with A revisions, nd. Numbered pages cut from notebook with many missing and 4 pages from exercise book.
[Prose fragments]. Ams/fragments of miscellaneous unidentified works, nd.
Mary [Campbell]. ALS to Tullah Hanley, 1957 June 19.
Mary Campbell. 8 ALS to *Dame* Edith Sitwell, 1 nd, 5 inc d, 1949 September 1, 1950 January 14.
Mary [Campbell]. 5 ALS to *[Dame]* Edith [Sitwell], _____ March 31, _____ November 3, 1950 February 4, 1950 February 24, 1951 June 8.
W[yndham] L[ewis], 1886-1957. ALI to Mary Campbell, 1936 Aug. 26.
Dylan Thomas, 1914-1953. [Broadcast] Poetic licence. Tccms (18pp), Tms/photocopy (23pp), 1950 December 13. Participants: W. R. Rodgers, Roy Campbell, George Barker, and Dylan Thomas.
[Dylan Thomas], 1914-1953. [Notes for a review of Roy Campbell's Light on a dark horse]. Ams with A revisions [16pp on 13ℓℓ], nd. Boxed.
[Terence Ian Fytton Armstrong], 1912- . Roy Campbell: Some bio-bibliographical notes by his friend John Gawsworth *[pseud.]*. Ams/first draft S "John Gawsworth" with A revisions (36pp), 1961 July.
[Terence Ian Fytton Armstrong], 1912- . Roy Campbell: Some bio-bibliographical notes by his friend John Gawsworth *[pseud.]*. Ams/second draft S "John Gawsworth" with A emendations [34pp], 1961 July.
Edmund [Charles] Blunden, 1896- . Roy Campbell: a poet's death. AmsS (2pp), Tms (3pp), Tccms (3pp), [1957].
Crane & Hawkins. TLS to *Dame* Edith Sitwell *re* Roy Campbell, 1955 March 9. Enclosed with this: TLS The Star to Edith Sitwell, 1955 March 8.
Herbert[Edward] Palmer, 1880-1961. AL/draft S to Roy Campbell, nd.
Hermann Peschmann, 1906- . [Review of] Poems of St. John of the Cross: Spanish text with a translation by Roy Campbell. Galley proof [1p], nd.
Denys Kilham Roberts. TLS to *Dame* Edith Sitwell, 1955 August 24. Attached to this: Clippings from the author *re* Roy Campbell.
Dame Edith Sitwell, 1887-1964. [Foreword to Collected Poems, Vol. III: Translation by Roy Campbell] Preface. Ams/draft S with A emendations [4pp], [c. 1959].
Dame Edith Sitwell, 1887-1964. [Review of] Selected poems by Roy Campbell. AmsS with few A revisions, nd.
Dame Edith Sitwell, 1887-1964. Roy Campbell. AmsS with few A revisions, nd.
[*Dame* Edith Sitwell], 1887-1964. [Roy Campbell]. Ams with A revisions, nd.
[*Dame* Edith Sitwell], 1887-1964. Roy Campbell. Ams with A revisions, nd. Bound.
Dame Edith Sitwell, 1887-1964. Roy Campbell. Tms (11 pp), [1957].
[*Dame* Edith Sitwell], 1887-1964. Roy Campbell. Ams/draft/inc with A revisions

[2pp], 1957.
[*Dame* Edith Sitwell], 1887-1964. Roy Campbell. Ams/inc, nd.
[*Dame* Edith Sitwell], 1887-1964. AL/draft to The New York Times Book Review editor *re* Roy Campbell, nd.

STUART CLOETE, 1897-

Letters

3 ALS, 5 TLS to PEN, directed to Hermon Ould, 3 nd, 1938-[1939].

JACK COPE, 1913-

Works

The boy and Mr. Katz [short story]. Ams with A emendations [12pp], nd. Written on verso of Stonewall's ghost. Ams with A emendations (29pp). No date.
A crack in the sky [short story]. Tccms with few A emendations and corrections (10pp], nd. Original title deleted: My friend. Contained in The Tame ox: Stories by Jack Cope.
Escape from love [short story]. Tms with few A emendations and corrections [18pp], nd. Contained in The Tame ox: Stories by Jack Cope.
Fair house. Tms and T/cc ms, nd. Bound.
The Flight [short story]. Tms with few A corrections (8pp), nd. Contained in The Tame ox: Stories by Jack Cope.
The golden oriole. T/cc ms with few A revisions, nd. Bound.
Kalahari Rose [short story]. Tccms with few A corrections (14pp), nd. Contained in The Tame ox: Stories by Jack Cope.
The Little missionary [short story]. Tms with A emendation and few A corrections (8pp), nd. Contained in The Tame ox: Stories by Jack Cope.
The man who doubted. Tccms with A emendations (17pp), nd.
No tea for Memsahib [short story]. Tms with few A corrections (18pp), nd. Contained in The Tame ox: Stories by Jack Cope.
One and a half [short story]. Tms with few A corrections (11pp), nd. Original title deleted: A Song of Africa. Contained in The Tame ox: Stories by JackCope.
The road to Ysterberg; a novel. T/cc ms with few A revisions, "First published 1959." Bound.
Roppie [short story]. Tccms with few A emendations (9pp), nd. Contained in The Tame ox: Stories by Jack Cope.
Say it with flowers [short story]. Tccms with few A emendations and corrections (7pp), nd. Contained in The Tame ox: Stories by Jack Cope.
A speck in the sun. Ams with many A revisions, nd. Bound.
Stonewall's ghost [short story]. Ams with A emendations (29pp), nd. Written on verso: The boy and Mr. Katz. Ams wtih A emendations [12pp]. No date.
Stonewall's ghost [short story]. Tccms with few A corrections (19pp), nd. Contained in The Tame ox: Stories by Jack Cope.
The Tame ox [short story]. Tms with few A corrections (12pp), nd. Contained in The Tame ox: Stories by Jack Cope.
The Tame ox: Stories by Jack Cope. Composite T and Tccms with A corrections and few A emendations and A printer's marks (vi, 166pp), 1960. Contents: The Tame ox.–A Crack in the sky.–Roppie.–One and a half.–The Whole of life.–The Little missionary.–Say it with flowers.–No tea for the Memsahib.–Escape from love.–Kalahari Rose.–Stonewall's ghost.–The flight.–Three women.
Three women [short story]. Tms with few A corrections (18pp), nd. Contained in

The Tame ox: Stories by Jack Cope.

The Whole of life [short story]. Tccms with few A corrections (14pp), nd. Contained in The Tame ox: Stories by Jack Cope.

Letters

TL to John Lehmann, 1960 June 27. Written on this: AN Barbara Cooper to substitute editor and AN by unidentified author.

[John Lehmann], 1907- .TccL to [Jack] Cope, 1960 August 8. By secretary.

Joseph [Jay] Jones, 1908- . TLS to William B. Todd *re* Cope ms, 1960 December 1.

NADINE GORDIMER, 1923-

Letters—Recipient

[Lehmann, John], 1907- . TccL to [Nadine] Gordimer, 1957 June 5.

DAN JACOBSON, 1929-

Letters-Recipient

[Lehmann, John], 1907- . 4 TccL to Dan Jacobson, 1954 December 31, 1955 August 18, 1955 November 2, 1958 January 10.

UYS KRIGE, 1910-

Works

The arrest. Ams with A revisions, 1958. Bound with this: Tms of the same.

The arrest. Tms with A revisions, nd. Bound with: Ams of the same.

The big shots. Ams with A revisions, 1958[?]. Bound.

The charcoal burners. AmsS with many A revisions, nd. Bound with this: The charcoal burners, AmsS with A revisions.

Death of the Zulu. AmsS with many A revisions, nd.

Has Africa, like America, a characteristic contribution to make to literature? Ams with many A revisions and T inserts, nd. Bound.

Two Daumiers. AmsS with A revisions, nd. Bound.

The way out. TmsS with A revisions and corrections, 1944 February-July. Bound.

The way out. Galley proofs with many A revisions, nd. Bound.

Letters

Joseph Jones. TLS to William B. Todd *re* Mss of Uys Krige and Jack Cope, 1960 November 29.

LAURENS VAN DER POST, 1906-

Letters

2 ALS to Merle Armitage, 1951 December 14, 1952 January 24.

ALS to John Boynton Priestley, 1964 November 9.

DORIS MAY LESSING, 1919-

Letters-Recipient

Rupert Croft-Cooke. TccL/reply to Doris [May] Lessing, 1952 December 15. Included with: TLS from Doris Lessing to Rupert Croft-Cooke.

[John Lehmann], 1907- . 2 TccL to Doris [May] Lessing, 1954 March 5, 1954 April 6. One by editorial assistant.

SARAH GERTRUDE MILLIN, 1889-1968

Letters

ALS to *Mrs.* [Marie Adelaide] (Belloc) Lowndes, 1926 January 24.

ALAN PATON, 1903-

Letters

ALS to [Herman Charles] Bosman, 1949 March 29.
TLS to [Gertrude (Maynard)] Anderson, 1949 May 3.
ALS, 4 TLS to Maxwell Anderson, 1948-1949.
TLS to Maxwell Anderson, 1948 October 7. Enclosure: [Alan Paton], TL/cc to Hugh Tracey, 1948 October 7.
ALS to Maxwell Anderson and [Gertrude (Maynard)] Anderson, 1949 April 19.
TL/copy to [(Charles) Scribner's Sons] [addressed to Scribner's Charles], nd.

Letters—Recipient

Maxwell Anderson, 1888-1959. TL/cc to Alan Paton, 1948 March 15.

WILLIAM CHARLES FRANKLYN PLOMER, 1903-

Works

At the supermarket [poem]. Ams (5pp), nd.
Bayswater and beyond. Tccms with A emendations and Tms/title page S with A note [9pp], 1950. Printed in Diversion: Twenty-two authors on the Lively Arts, edited by John Satro.
Copy. 2 Tmss (3pp each), 2 Tccmss, one with A revisions (3pp each), nd.
The devil-dancers. TmsI (2pp), nd.
A dodo in every bus by Robert Pagan *[pseud.]*. Tms (10pp), nd.
Double lives. Edmund [Charles] Blunden, 1896- .[Review of] Double lives: An autobiography by William Plomer. Galley proof [1p], nd.
V[ictor] S[awdon] Pritchett, 1900- . [Broadcast: Book Talk] Book review [of Double lives by William Plomer; Why was I Killed by Rex Warner; Thorofare by Christopher Morley; The unknown army by Nikolaus Basseches; A book of Russian Verse, edited by C. M. Bowra]. Tccms S radio script (7pp), [c. 1943].
The last train. AmsS (3pp), nd.
A lost face. TmsI [1p], nd.
Manners in the machine age. Ams with A revisions [18pp, 10x16cm], nd. Broadcast talk.
Museum pieces. AmsS with A revisions and A notes, one initialed. [552pp], 1949-1951. Original draft. Included with this: A note S *re* manuscripts of his works, [1p], 1961 November 27. Boxed.
Palmyra. Ams (8pp), nd.
Pas avant! by Robert Pagan *[pseud.]*. AmsS (18pp), Tms (7pp), nd.
Q[ueen] M[ary] and the Norwich croppers [poem]. Ams/first draft with extensive A revisions [4pp], 1952 Summer.
Queen Mary and the Norwich croppers [poem]. Ams with A revisions (2pp), [1952].
Queen Mary and the Norwich croppers. AmsS (2pp), nd.
[Reader's report on] Plaintales of the squirearchy by Nigel Heseltine. AmsI (4pp), nd.
[Reader's report on] The poetry of justice by Oliver Walker. AmsI (3pp), nd.
[Reader's report on] When the wind blows by Frank Sargeson. Ams (3pp), nd.

Review of Collected poems of William Barnes. Ams/draft and notes [13pp on 10ℓℓ], 1962 July.
[Review of] Edmund Blunden: A selection of his poetry and prose made by Kenneth Hopkins. Mimeo radio script (9pp), 1950 December 21 [broadcast date].
Seventeen faces. TmsI [1p], nd.
Visiting the caves. TmsI [1p], nd.
You must have two hats: A conversation with a civil servant by Robert Pagan *[pseud.]*. AmsS with A emendations and deletions (17pp), nd.

Letters
ALS to Edmund [Charles Blunden], 1952 February 23.
ALS to Jocelyn Brooke, 1958 May 16.
ALS to Richard Church, 1965 April 1.
ALS to Richard [Church], 1966 October 8.
3 ALS to [Barbara] Cooper, 1945 September 12, 1946 July 30, 1948 June 16.
ALS to Barbara [Cooper], 1952 April 5.
ALS to Maurice [Cranston], 1960 September 3.
ALS to Maurice Cranston *re* Plomer's review of a book by Ivan Roe, 1950 May 31.
ALS to [Kenneth] Hopkins, 1949 June 25.
49 ALS, 4 TLS, 1 APCS, 2 APCI to John Lehmann, 6 nd, 4 inc d, 1935-1949. Included with these: Biographical sketch of Robert Pagan *[pseud.]*.
26 ALS, 1 AN to John Lehmann, 2 nd, 1949-1960.
5 ALS to *Mrs.* [Marie Adelaide] (Belloc) Lowndes, 1946 February 26, 1946 April 30, 1946 June 6, 1946 June 10, 1946 August 2.
10 ALS, 2 APCS, 1 ACPI to *Lady* Ottoline [Violet Anne (Cavendish-Bentinck)] Morrell, 6 nd, 1 inc d, 1932-1934.
5 ALS, 1 APCI to Charles Osborne, 1 nd, 1958-1963.
6 ALS to [Jacob] Schwartz, 1962.
ALS, AL/inc, TLS to [Rolfe Arnold] Scott-James, _____September 28, 1934 September 1, 1936 April 3.
ALS to [Rolfe Arnold] Scott-James, 1939 March 29.
5 ALS to *[Dame]* Edith [Sitwell], 1945 December 10, 1949 September 14, 1954 June 11, 1957 August 24, 1958 September 1.
9 ALS, 1 ALS/inc, 1 Christmas card to *[Dame]* Edith [Sitwell], 1 nd, 1947-1957.
TLS to [Virginia Woolf], 1930 January 20.
ALS to [James] Wright, 1958 October 11.

Letters–Recipient
Unidentified author. TLS "Ernestine" to William Plomer, nd.
[The British Broadcasting Corporation]. 2 TccLI Z. A. Bokhari to William [Charles Franklyn] Plomer, 1941 September 12, 1941 September 19. September 19 TccLI initialed by secretary. For John Lehmann's information.
Cambridge University Press. TLS to [William Charles Franklyn Plomer] R[obert] Pagan, *[pseud.]*, 1948 June 14.
Ivy Compton-Burnett, 1892- . ALS to [William Charles Franklyn Plomer], 1940 February 9.
Graham Greene, 1904- . ALS to [William Charles Franklyn] Plomer, nd.
Florence [Emily (Dugdale)] Hardy, d.1937. ALS to [William Charles Franklyn] Plomer, 1934 March 17.

John Lehmann, 1907- . 43 TccL to William [Charles Franklyn] Plomer, 1 nd, 2 inc d, 1934-1948. 4 by secretary. Included with these: A note I by Lehmann, 1940 July 5.
John Lehmann, 1907- . 17 TccL to William [Charles Franklyn] Plomer, 1950-1960. One by secretary. Included with these: ANI to Barbara Cooper.
The London Magazine. T invoice to William Plomer with his A receipt, 1954 January 1 [date of receipt].
W[illiam] S[omerset] Maugham, 1874- . ALS to [William Charles Franklyn] Plomer, _____ September 30. Extracted from Ms of Plomer's Museum Pieces.
J[ohn] Middleton Murry, 1889-1957. 2 ALS to [William Charles Franklyn] Plomer, 1929 July 11, 1929 September 21. Letterhead: The New Adelphi.
[Dame] Edith [Sitwell], 1887-1964. A/draft S of telegram[?] to [William] Plomer, nd.
Virginia [(Stephen)] Woolf, 1882-1941. 15 ALS, 11 ALI, 1 TLS, 5 APCS, 3 APCI to William [Charles Franklyn] Plomer, 16 nd, 10 inc d, 1929-1940.

Miscellaneous
John Lehmann, 1907- . [Broadcast] Signposts in English literature—William Plomer. Tms/fragment [1p], Tccms/fragment S [1p], nd. Used also as part of Seven free spirits in English literature.
[John Lehmann], 1907- . [Broadcasts] Turning over a new leaf. 11 T and Tccms/radio scripts with A revisions, notes and additions [57pp], 1941. First script incomplete. Some scripts have Tms or printed selections by the subject author attached. Contents: (1) Introductory.—(2) Cecil Day Lewis.—(3) Henry Green.—(4) Laurie Lee.—(5) Gordon Jeffery.—(6) Stephen Spender.—(7) Rosamund Lehmann.—(8) V. S. Pritchett.—(9) William Plomer.—(10) B. L. Coombes.—(11) Rex Warner.
J[ohn] L[ehmann], 1907- . Seven free spirits in modern English literature. Tccms I (43pp), 1948 December.

OLIVE SCHREINER, 1855-1920

Works
The dawn of civilisation: The causes of war. Ams with A revisions (130pp), [1920].
The dawn of civilisation: Introduction. Tms with A revisions [9pp], [1920]. Written on title page: A note I by her husband.
[The dawn of civilisation]: Remedies for war. Ams wtih A revisions (47pp), [1920].
From man to man. AmsS/inc with A revisions (26pp), nd. Signed with pseudonym Ralph Iron.
[From man to man; or, Perhaps only]. Ams/inc with A revisions and A note [168pp], 1886-1887 (Alassio, Italy).
Journal: Rattel's Hoek. Ams/inc [8pp], 1876 July 24-September 23.
Thoughts on South Africa. Composite T, Tcc and printed msS/inc, with A revisions [157pp], 1896-1901. Title on this ms: Stray thoughts on South Africa.
Three dreams in a desert: Extracts. Tms/copy (4pp), nd.
Trooper Peter Halket of Mashonalan. Galley Proofs (19pp), [1897]. Boxed.
Undine. Tms/unfinished (111pp), nd.
Will. Ams/copy [2pp], 1892 December. Included with this: AL/inc and ALS/inc *re* the will, apparently to Havelock Ellis.
Workers. AmsS with A revisions [2pp on 1ℓ], 1887 April 16. Signed with

pseudonym Ralph Iron.

Letters

2 ALI/drafts to [unidentified recipient], 1885 December 28.
ALS to [unidentified recipients] "My dear children," nd.
[Extracts from letters to Mrs. John Brown]. TL/copies/extracts [2pp], 1893-1894. Title on this: Chapter V; additional letters.
2 ALS to [Frederick] Chapman, 1886 September 16, 1886 November 2.
[Letters to Havelock Ellis]. Microfilm copy [1 reel], nd.
200 ALS to Havelock Ellis, 1884-1907. Parts of some letters missing.
7 ALS, 1 APCS to Richard Garnett, 2nd, 1885-1889.
2 ALS to [Frank] Harris, nd, 1888 August 23.
7 ALS, 1 APCS to Joan Hodgson, 7 nd, 1 inc d. Two directed also to John Hodgson. Signed Aunt Olive.
[Letters to John L. Hodgson]. 55 ALS, 9 ALI, 2 AL, 2 AL/inc, 13 APCS, 15 APCI, 88 nd, 1914-[1920].
2 TL/copies to Alfred Mattison, 1896 April 13, 1897 August 4.
ALS to ____ Norman, 1884 May 22.
APCS to Frank Padmore, 1887 September 9 [postmark].
To [William Philip Schreiner] "Will." TccL/copy, 1875 October 30.
ALS to Arthur Symons, nd.

Letters–Recipient

Havelock Ellis, 1859-1939. 177 ALS to Olive Schreiner, 9 nd, 147 inc d, 21 1884-[19]20.
3 ALS to Olive [Schreiner], nd (Monday), 1884 August 24, 1884 October 24.
Sir H[enry] Rider Haggard, 1856-1925. ALS to [Olive] Schreiner, 1884 October 21.
The London Library, [Receipt to] Olive Schreiner. Printed DS [1p], 1884 October 20.
[*Mrs.* Schreiner]. 2 ALS "Mother" to [Olive Schreiner], ____ August 18, 1886 December 27.
Arthur Symons, 1865-1945. ALS to [Olive] Schreiner, ____ April 25.

Miscellaneous

[Unidentified author], [Review of] Dreams [by Olive] Schreiner. Page proofs with A revisions and insertions [27pp], nd.
Esilda Cawood to *Mrs.* Schreiner. TccL/copy, 1888 April 8. Olive Schreiner's mother.
The London Library, [Receipt to] Olive Schreiner. Printed DS [1p], 1884 October 20.
Havelock Ellis, 1859-1939, "Olive Schreiner." A ms, 1884 June 26.
E. S. Sachs, Talk [at] Olive Schreiner Centenary Memorial. 2 Tccms/copies (5pp; 6pp), 1955 March 29.